The Lost Leadbeater's Possums

Tales from Tim Faulkner

Illustrated by **Elin Matilda**

Australian **G**EOGRAPHIC

Not very far away,
in the hills behind a big town,
once lived some possums in a tree,
right up near the crown.

Not very long ago,
scientists thought they were gone.
All the possums had disappeared,
something had gone very wrong.

This is why the possums cry
at night when we're asleep.

The Leadbeater's possums had lived in tall trees
in the highlands down south where it's cold.
They built their homes in empty tree hollows,
in a forest that was big and healthy and old.

But when the scientists went looking,
all they were able to see
were the dangers and threats
that had forced the possums to flee.

This is why the possums cry
at night when we're asleep.

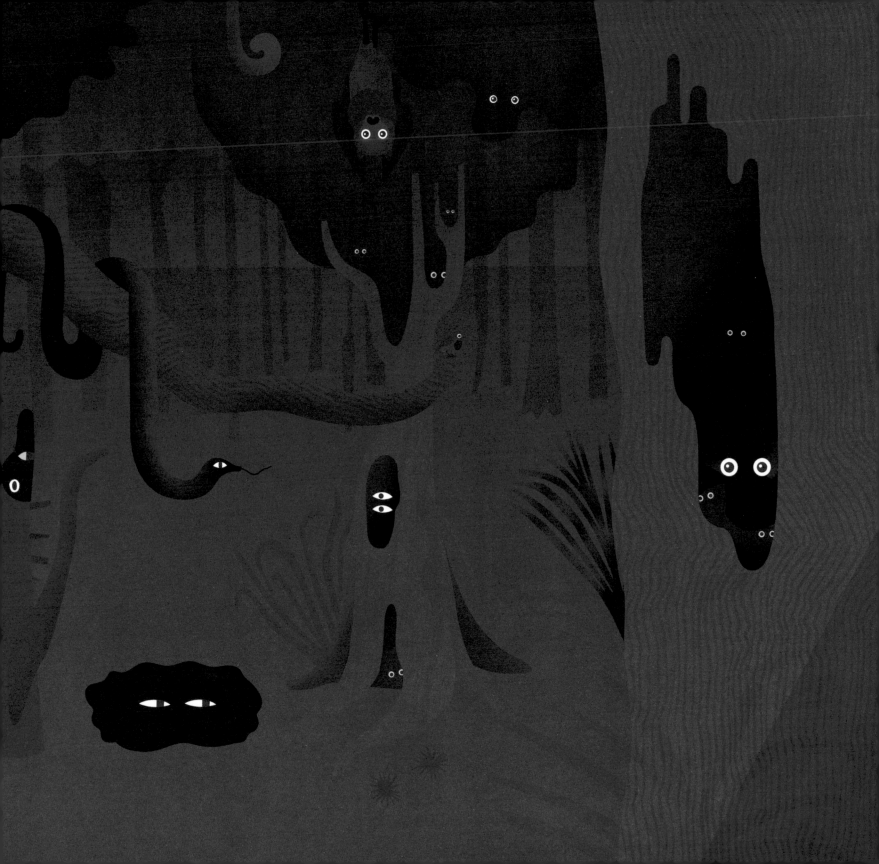

The first threat is bushfire, the scientists know.
Every time a fire starts to blaze,
the possums bolt and scatter
and their homes burn down in the smoky haze.

The scientists and firefighters made a vow
that they would try to stop the fires,
hoping the Leadbeater's possums
would return home to their shires.

This is why the possums cry
at night when we're asleep.

The other threat is logging,
when they cut the forest down
and every time it happens,
the possums surely frown.

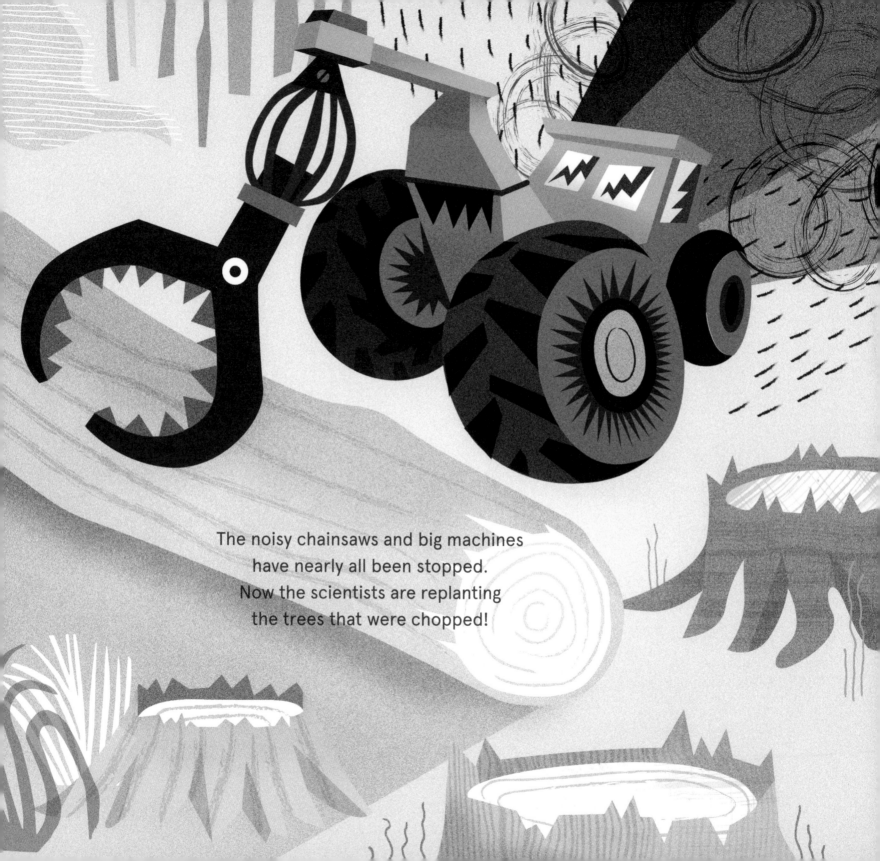

The noisy chainsaws and big machines
have nearly all been stopped.
Now the scientists are replanting
the trees that were chopped!

This is why the possums cry
at night when we're asleep.

Not long after a scientist went walking
through the forest, dark and scary.
He spotted something move in the trees,
something grey and small and hairy!

He aimed his torch up in the branches
and the furball turned around,
it was a Leadbeater's Possum,
rediscovered and now found!

This is why the possums smile
at night when we're asleep.

Being home was such a joy,
all the possums were excited.
The scientists all celebrated,
they were just so delighted!

Finding them was just the start
and now the hard work must begin,
to protect the animals and forest
and the trees that they live in!

This is why the possums sing
at night when we're asleep.

This is great news for possums and
even better now that you know.
The future is in good hands
but there's a long, long way to go.

Every time you go outside
and look up in the trees,
think of the Leadbeater's possums
and be kind to their old forest, please!

Appearance

They are small marsupials weighing up to 160 grams – about the same as a small apple! They measure between 15 and 17 centimetres in length and their tail is almost as long as their body. They are a greyish-brown colour and have a unique black stripe down their back.

Leadbeater's possum

Other name: Fairy possum
Status: Critically endangered

Extinction

The rare Leadbeater's possum was officially declared extinct in the 1950s. In 1961, however, naturalist Eric Wilkinson stumbled upon a population east of Melbourne, and the species was re-listed.

Location

They are native to Australia and found in the central highlands of Victoria.

Diet
They eat mainly sap, but also snack on small insects, acacia gum and honeydew.

Habitat
They live in cool, swampy areas surrounded by plenty of eucalyptus and acacia trees.

Close relatives
The sugar glider, squirrel glider, yellow-bellied glider, mahogany glider and striped possum are all close relatives.

Saving the possums
Researchers at the Yellingbo Nature Conservation Reserve, Victoria, are currently working to find the best ways to keep these possums alive. Only about 1500 Leadbeater's possums still exist.

Shelter
Leadbeater's possums make nests of shredded bark inside tree hollows. They sleep for up to 16 hours a day.

State emblem
The Leadbeater's possum is the animal emblem for Victoria.

Life cycle
Females can give birth up to twice a year. Babies are born usually two weeks after mating and are then carried in their mothers pouch for up to 12 weeks. The young then spend another four weeks in the nest.

Threats
Fire, logging and events that damage their habitat are some of the major threats to these possums.

Namesake
They are named after John Leadbeater, the Director of Taxidermy at the Museum of Victoria between 1857 and 1888.

Tim Faulkner

Wrestling a saltwater crocodile, wrangling a deadly taipan and milking a funnel-web spider is all in a days work for Tim Faulkner! He could do all that and still find time to release a blue-tongue lizard, tag a wild platypus and save the Tasmanian devil from extinction!

Tim is a Director and Head of Conservation at the Australian Reptile Park in Somersby, NSW, and The Devil Ark at Barrington Tops, NSW. Australian Geographic Conservationist of the Year (2015), Tim features in numerous TV shows, including his own **Wild Life of Tim Faulkner**, showcasing Australian wildlife to the world.

Tim developed a love for the Australian bush and wildlife at a young age. He is proud to be sharing these stories with children, with the hope they will feel the same love for native creatures.

The Lost Leadbeater's Possums

First edition published by Australian Geographic in 2016
An imprint of Bauer Media Ltd
54 Park Street, Sydney, NSW 2000
Telephone +61 2 9263 9813
Email editorial@ausgeo.com.au
www.ausgeo.com.au

Australian Geographic customer service
1300 555 176 from within Australia (local call rate)
+61 2 8667 5295 from outside Australia

Author: Tim Faulkner
Illustrator: Elin Matilda
Art director: Mike Ellott
Designer: Mike Rossi
Editor: Lauren Smith
Sub-editor: Amy Russell
Proofreader: Gemma Chilton

Publisher, Specialist Division: Cornelia Schulze
Publisher: Jo Runciman
Australian Geographic editor-in-chief: Chrissie Goldrick
Australian Geographic editor: John Pickrell

A portion of the funds from the sale of this book go to support the Australian Geographic Society,
a not-for-profit organisation dedicated to sponsoring conservation,
scientific research, adventures and expeditions.